Sex ti...
by guys

Sex tips for girls
by guys

LONDON, NEW YORK, MUNICH,
MELBOURNE, DELHI

Project Editor Laura Palosuo
Editor Becky Alexander
Project Art Editor Wendy Bartlet
Designer Nigel Wright
Managing Editor Penny Smith
Managing Art Editor Marianne Markham
Production Editor Clare McLean
Senior Production Controller Seyhan Esen
Creative Technical Support Sonia Charbonnier
Publisher Peggy Vance

First published in Great Britain in 2012
by Dorling Kindersley Limited,
80 Strand, London WC2R 0RL

Penguin Group (UK)
2 4 6 8 10 9 7 5 3 1
001 – 182625 – Jan/2012
Copyright © 2011 Dorling Kindersley Limited
All rights reserved.

A CIP catalogue record for this book
is available from the British Library.
ISBN 978-1-4053-9400-0

Printed and bound in Singapore by
Tien Wah Press

Discover more at
www.dk.com

contents

intro

OK, we'll let you in on a secret. It's easy to make a **guy happy** in bed. Often, just the fact that you're **pleased to be in bed** is enough to put **joy in our hearts.** So imagine what it's like when you want to **indulge us** with the tips and treats in this book. **Pure heaven**.

duction

Whether you use this book to **dip into at random** or you work through every single tip **(hint: we'd like that)**, expect to have a very **happy and contented** man on your hands.

Now, isn't it time for bed...?

tou

ch
me

sweet &

Like you, we love a bit of sexy foreplay before we get down to serious business.

"She came to bed **wearing just a feather boa**. She use

sensual

"...to **caress every bit of my body**. I still think about it."

man pa

We don't often **pamper** our **bodies** so whe

Take a **bath together**. Sit behind and **massage his back** and **chest** with **bubbles** or shower gel.

mpering

ou do it for us it feels like a **very special treat**.

 Rub massage oil **all over** him. Use firm, **confident strokes,** then try some light, **teasing strokes**.

mmmmm

You already know the headline erogenous zones. But don't forget to show some attention to our less famous parts – the ones that make us go "mmmm" with quiet satisfaction.

"**She kisses me** on my jawline and then slowly **works her way down** the side of my neck. **It feels amazing**."

zones

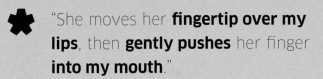 "She moves her **fingertip over my lips**, then **gently pushes** her finger **into my mouth**."

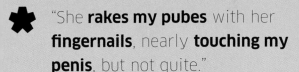 "She **rakes my pubes** with her **fingernails**, nearly **touching my penis**, but not quite."

very

Taking us in hand is a skill we'll love you for. It's thrilling to feel your touch. And that means casual, friendly strokes as well as full-on handjobs. Stroke, caress, and squeeze us with soft, bare hands – or wear sexy gloves for a different touch.

handy

✿ **Say hello** by sneaking your **hands around his waist** from behind. Trace the **outline of his package** while pressing **your breasts** against his back. Now **slip your fingers** into **his pants** and tease him with a **few light strokes**.

✿ **Join him** for a **shower**, squirt some shower gel into **your palms** and **massage his penis** using long strokes.

two

We like it when you mix things up a bit. Even something simple like using two hands rather than one makes us sit up and take notice.

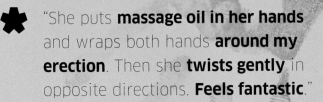

handers

✼ "She puts **massage oil in her hands** and wraps both hands **around my erection**. Then she **twists gently** in opposite directions. **Feels fantastic**."

✼ "**She does this great move** where she links her fingers together and then her hands **glide up and down**."

✼ "She sits **between my legs** and **strokes my penis** hand over hand. **So sexy!**"

f-

There's one particular part of the penis – the F-spot – that makes us really stand to attention. It's that place on the underside where the foreskin joins the penis, A.K.A. the "banjo string".

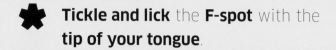 **Tickle and lick** the **F-spot** with the **tip of your tongue**.

 When **giving a handjob**, apply some extra **thumb pressure** to the **F-spot** as your hand **glides up and down**.

spotting

 Lick your **index finger**, then draw **wet tiny circles** on his **F-spot**.

happy

As much as we love a bit of hand-to-penis attention during foreplay, we sometimes like a handjob to go all the way. Lying back and looking forward to a happy ending can be sheer bliss.

 "There's **something thrilling** about the way she literally **takes me in hand** and **takes control**."

endings

 "When I'm on the **home stretch**, I like **hard, fast pumps** around the head that don't **change in speed**."

 "**It's a cliché**, but it drives me wild to **come on her breasts**."

ball

Our balls are very close to the dancefloor, but they don't always get invited to the party. Which is a shame. They're packed with nerve endings and we love it when you play with them.

play

✳ Try **treating the boys** to any or all of these: **barely-there cat licks; sucks** and **kisses**; light grazing with **your fingernails**; or a nice **snug hold** in the **palm of your hand**.

✳ We're also fans of **sex positions** that are **ball-inclusive**. Try sitting **on top** and **sliding back and forth**. Also, when you stand up and bend over, **our crown jewels give you a gentle slap** with each inward thrust.

no-man's

 Name one part of a man that rarely gets touched.

 The stretch of skin behind his balls. Men call it the "taint" because "it 'aint balls and it 'aint arse".

land

 Make it **your mission** to discover this lost erogenous zone: **caress his taint** with **your fingers** or **tongue**.

 The taint is also an **excellent resting spot** when you want to calm him down **during a blowjob**. Treat him to **some soft kisses** down there before you return to the main action.

We love it when you do a little exploring down under. Let your fingers trail down the penis, over the balls, and do a little teasing of the anus.

under

✱ **Stroke** or **circle his anus** with a lightly **lubed finger**. Experiment with applying a **little more pressure** or venturing a **short way inside**.

✱ Always pay attention to **his body language** and let it be your guide: tightly **clenched buttocks** means **"no thanks"** while **lifting his pelvis** toward you says: **"go right ahead"**.

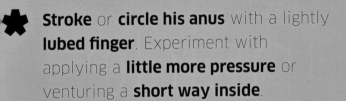

umop

inside
job

Know your G-spot? Well, we've got one too. It's called the P-spot and, if you know where to find it, you can unlock a mind-popping orgasm.

Gently insert your finger into **his anus**. **Reach up and forward** (towards his belly). Let his **moans of pleasure** guide you to the **right spot.** While you're busy in the basement, get him to **pleasure himself** up top. Or give him a **blowjob**. Either way, the results will be **bed-rocking**.

getting

Bum, butt, ass... whatever you **call it** we love you **touching it**

cheeky

 Give him a **bare buttock massage**. Use your palms to **press**, **pound**, **and pummel**, and then change the pace by **tracing your fingertips** lightly across his skin for a **sexy contrast**.

 Try hands-free: rub massage oil over **your belly and breasts** and then slither up and down on his back and backside. **Warning: he may roll over and grab you...**

master class

10/10

If you're unsure of how a man really wants to be handled there's a simple way to find out: ask for a demo. The chances are he will be very willing to oblige.

 "It was **so sexy**. She put her **hand on top of mine** while I **played with my penis and balls**."

 "She laid **in between my legs** and asked to **watch me masturbate**. I loved it! It's usually **me who tries to watch**!"

nipple

Our nipples may not be quite as sensitive as yours, but they're still a hot spot. Like you, we get more sensation if you prepare the ground. So here are some nipple play tips!

play

❄ We **like it** when you **mix up the sensations**. Start by **licking**, then try **nibbling**. Or **stroke gently** with your fingertips, followed by a **tweak**.

❄ Try **licking a nipple** then **blowing** across it to give us the **good kind of goosebumps**.

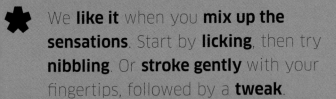

heady
sens

Not that kind of head. The scalp. A head massage will relax us and leave us putty in your hands.

 Sit on the floor with **his head** in your lap. **Glide your fingertips** firmly along his hairline. Now **circle his temples**. Repeat until **he purrs**.

ations

✻ Do this in your **underwear** or **naked** for an **extra wow factor**.

✻ **Finish your massage** by leaning forward to deliver **a passionate kiss**.

✻ Try giving a **head massage** when we are **face-down** in **your lap**.

toe play

Despite its dodgy reputation, toe play can make grown men groan. Why? Because it reminds us of blowjobs. So ramp up the associations with lots of licking and sucking.

 Give us **a sexy look** while you do **some mouth toe play**. Add some playful licks, and let your **lips slide up and down** with **titillating slowness**.

A shared bath (or hot tub) is a great venue **for toe-sucking**. Sit at opposite ends and **take his foot firmly** in hand. (You can wash his feet first then too...)

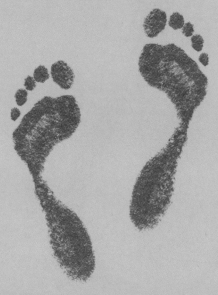

no

If you've got long hair, let it trail over his chest.

handers

Who says a massage must be done with hands alone? Feel free to rub other parts of your body against us too.

 Try **getting on all-fours** above him and **caressing him** with your **breasts**. The **soft, stroking** sensations will **drive him to distraction**.

 Play footsie. Your feet can deliver amazing sensations too - try using your toes to **lightly caress his penis**.

rough &

Sometimes we like it playful; a bit of rough-and-tumble turns us on. And we really like it when you're the Boss.

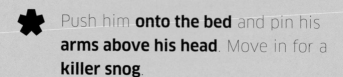 Push him **onto the bed** and pin his **arms above his head**. Move in for a **killer snog**.

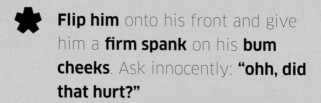 **Flip him** onto his front and give him a **firm spank** on his **bum cheeks**. Ask innocently: **"ohh, did that hurt?"**

ready

getting

What do girls have that guys don't?
Long fingernails of course. They can
deliver some sexy sensations.

✳ "**She straddles me** when I'm on my
front and **lightly grazes my back** with
her nails. Makes me **shiver**."

✳ "We were getting **pretty rough** and
playful – I woke up the **next morning**
with **scratches** all over **my chest**. A
hot reminder of the night before!"

scratchy

triple

If you want to make him cross-eyed with pleasure, try this advanced massage trick.

Sit on your **naked man**. Sweep your palms over **his chest and belly with** tantalizing slowness. Work your way down and **massage his penis,** too.

treat

 When **his flagpole** is firmly **raised, climb on board**. Continue **stroking his chest** with your palms.

 Move **up and down** in sync with your hands as they **travel over his body. That** is a **thorough massage**.

tea

se
me

tongue

Your tongue is one of your sexiest assets. It's warm and wet and we love everything it can do. Kissing, blowjobs, neck nuzzling, toe sucking…yes, we are big fans.

teasing

✳ "We were **lying on the sofa** watching TV and she raised **my hand** to **her mouth**. She **sucked each of my fingers** in turn. **Amazing**."

✳ "She **nibbled my earlobe** and I felt **her tongue** darting in my ear. Then she **took me to bed** – fantastic."

✳ "She makes me **lie on my front** – then she **bites, licks,** and **nibbles** her way down my body. **Best massage ever**."

it's in

Never underestimate the **power of a kiss:** It sends a **clear signal** that you **want us**.

her kiss

* Cup his face **sweetly** in **your hands**, give him your best **smouldering look**, and **kiss gently**. Feel your way **into his mouth** with your **tongue**. Make your **kiss long** and **sensual** – if he pulls away, **tell him "more..."**.

* **Ramp things up** by pushing him **against the nearest wall** and giving him a **sexy snog**. Press your **pelvis hard against his** for a guaranteed **erection-starter**.

tongue slap

This has a slightly kinky feel to it, which is probably why we like it so much. All you need is a sexy attitude, a wet tongue, and a naked man.

 Grasp his penis and stick **your tongue** out as far as you can. Fix him with a **wicked look**. Now **slap the head of his penis** against the **flat of your tongue**. Repeat a few times, but not too fast – you want to build up lots of **sexy anticipation** between each slap. Visually, this **looks amazingly dirty**. Plus the **wet slap** feels **fantastic**.

U-spott

Our U-spot (the eye of the penis) may be small, but it can bring us a lot of joy, so please give it a little attention.

ng

✳ We **like it** when you give the U-spot some **special attention** at the **start of a blowjob**; we are still **nice and sensitive** then, so can feel everything.

✳ Position the **tip of your tongue** right above the **head of the penis**. Hover for a few seconds then draw **tiny circles around the U-spot** with the tip of your tongue. (Look up and add a **cheeky wink** if you like.)

cool se

When things are getting hot and feverish, cooling things down can send a bolt of pleasure through us.

 During a **back massage**, run your warm, **wet tongue** down **his spine**. Then blow cool air along the same path. Other superb **spots for licking and blowing** are his **neck and nipples**.

ɪsations

 To **spice up a blowjob**, pull away and blow a long, **cool stream of air** over **his manhood**. His hot **skin will tingle** in a way that **makes him gasp**.

the first rule of blowjobs

no

Except **gentle nibbling** by prior arrangement.

teeth

a
trip
down
south

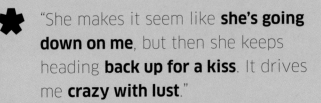

Sometimes it's about the journey and not just the destination. As your gorgeous lips travel down south, we love to be teased and tantalized on the way.

"She makes it seem like **she's going down on me**, but then she keeps heading **back up for a kiss**. It drives me **crazy with lust**."

"She **crawled slowly** over my body **on all-fours** – her head facing my feet. She told me, 'Look but don't touch'."

"She kissed my toes, then worked her way up the **inside of my leg**. I could feel her **hot breath on my penis**."

quick

quick
slow

This is all about surprise and anticipation. And it sure beats ballroom dancing.

 Do **nine quick shallow thrusts** during a **blowjob**, then on your tenth stroke, **plunge your lips** as far down **his shaft** as you can. Keep everything **hot, wet, and slick** and see him **lose control**.

swallow

To swallow or not to swallow?

door entry

 This is best when you are **extremely aroused** so get him to **lavish you with sexual favours first**. Massage lubricant between your cheeks and along his shaft. Take insertion **one slow centimetre at a time**. Relax your muscles and breathe out as he enters.

chain him up

This is bondage for beginners. No chains or cuffs required – a silk scarf and a coat hook are all you need.

Start both standing up. After a **passionate snog**, get him to cross his wrists. **Bind them together** with a scarf. Push his hands **above his head** and loop the scarf over a handy coat **hook just above him**. Slink down his body, undo his flies, and take him **firmly in hand** (or **mouth**).

peep

Spying on a sexy scene is a classic schoolboy fantasy. It's also one many of us still cherish, even though we might not admit it.

show

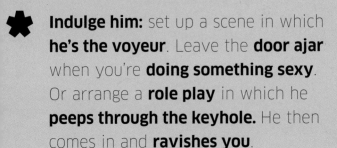

✱ **Indulge him:** set up a scene in which **he's the voyeur**. Leave the **door ajar** when you're **doing something sexy**. Or arrange a **role play** in which he **peeps through the keyhole.** He then comes in and **ravishes you**.

✱ Great **peep show scenes** include: drying your body after showering; **caressing body lotion** into your naked skin (especially your breasts); and **pleasuring yourself** with a sex toy.

hello

Shake-up sex with a scorchingly hot role play. The plot is simple: you're two strangers meeting in a bar. You find yourselves in the grip of an electric attraction that you just can't ignore...

"**I hardly recognised her**. She'd changed her hair and was wearing this mind-blowing dress. **I couldn't believe my luck**."

stranger

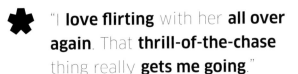
✳ "I **love flirting** with her **all over again**. That **thrill-of-the-chase** thing really **gets me going**."

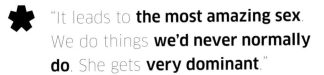
✳ "It leads to **the most amazing sex**. We do things **we'd never normally do**. She gets **very dominant**."

in sus

You know how blindfolded sex works? Taking away sight enhances the other senses. Well, try going a step further: take away his hearing too.

 Put a **blindfold on him**, and plug him into **some funky music** on a pair of headphones. Now treat him to all manner of **kinky delights**. The suspense alone will keep him rigid with excitement. **Kiss, lick and nibble**.

pense

in a bind

We know you mean business when you come to bed with a pair of handcuffs. The thrill for us is that it takes dominance to the next level. If we're tied to the bed/chair/table, surrender really is our only option.

✸ Try **cuffing or tying him** wrist-to-wrist and ankle-to-ankle. Or bind him to the bedposts in the notorious **spread-eagle position** – you can access all his best bits this way.

✸ **Tease him mercilessly** with **tongue flicks, kisses, bites, sucks, and strokes**. Or, if you fancy some me-time, just **hop on top** and enjoy.

on tape

Hand him a roll of bondage tape and ask him to "dress" you. (Bondage tape is like sticky tape except it sticks only to itself so there is no pain involved!)

 His job is to fashion the **tightest, kinkiest dress** by winding the tape around **your naked body**. Suggest he leaves gaps at certain strategic points so he can **kiss and touch** you. If you're fresh out of bondage tape, **try clingfilm instead**.

Use your bondage tape to **tie his wrists** to the bed. Or behind his back. Then he is **completely at your mercy**.

three in

Threesomes: we make no apology, they're right up there in our list of hot fantasies. So if you want to make us crazy with pleasure, suggest some girl-on-boy-on-girl action.

the bed

 "**It started** after a **party**. The **three of us** made out **for hours**... it was the most **memorable night of my life**."

 "**She and her friend** put a blindfold on me. After each **kiss, lick, or bite**, they asked: '**Guess who**?'"

a touch of

Something about the look, smell, and feel of leather shouts "kinky" to us.

 For beginner level kinkiness, wear a **leather belt**. He can **grab hold** of it **mid-action**.

 For **advanced raunch**, come to bed in a **leather corset** or **dog collar**.

leather

the first rule of S&M

don't

Before you throw yourself into some **bondage, spanking or S&M**, agree a "get out" word beforehand. Choose something silly, like "**lollipop**". Something sensible like "**stop**" might not work because you might want to shout that as **part of the kinky fun...**

stop!

slavish devotion

Make him smile by offering to be his sex slave for the night. Tell him he can ask for whatever he wants (within reason). We will return the favour.

✱ Get **dressed up** for the occasion. Try **wearing** a Venetian-style **masquerade mask**. It looks **gorgeously exotic** and **alluring**, and helps you both get into the **role play**.

✱ If **total submission** ticks boxes for both of you, start on all fours and **crawl seductively** in his direction. Address him as "**master**" and **see what happens...**

going

Going to be apart for a while? Send him off with a sexy video of the two of you for him to discover in his suitcase.

away
gift

✱ **Make your film** without him knowing. Film you both in a stunning sequence of **positions and moves**. It'll make for explosive viewing later.

✱ Or try the old-school option: tuck a **sexy photograph** into his wash bag for a **bedtime surprise**.

party night

You don't have to be into group sex and swinging to throw a sex party. You just need the two of you, a locked bedroom door, a supply of sexy goodies, and a naughty attitude.

 "**One night a month** we go over the top: **sex toys, videos, costumes, cocktails, and massage oil**."

 "Most of the time we're **sweet and loving** in bed, but every now and then, **we agree that anything goes**."

after

The next best thing to having **really great sex** is, in our opinion, thinking about the really great sex that we've had. In fact, sometimes **it's all we think about**. A good sex memory will last us until we're old and grey. Or at least until we make the next one.

glow

I once had incredible web cam sex. My girlfriend **video-called me and stripped**. When she was nearly naked her best friend came in and kissed her. Gorgeous!

My girlfriend surprised me with a **quickie just before we went** out. I grinned for the rest of the night.

I told my girlfriend I'd always fantasized about **sex on the beach**. So she indulged me by throwing a pop-up tent onto the sand and **pulling me inside**. She pushed me on my back, said "sshhh", and just climbed on top.

The **naughtiest** present I ever had was a Japanese sex chair. Instead of a seat it had wide elastic bands so that my girlfriend could sit on top while I penetrated her from below. **Weightless sex is sublime**.

My girlfriend knows I've got a fetish for girls in kinky nurse uniforms. So she threw a surprise party with a nurse/doctor dress code. **I was in heaven**.

My girlfriend once asked me to make an erotic film of her while **staying fully dressed** and concentrating on the camera work. She gave the **sexiest performance I've ever seen**. Then we had amazingly fast sex on the carpet!

My girlfriend and I went to see a **sex show** when abroad. We both agreed it was really seedy. Then we went back to our hotel room and **had the most fantastic sex**.

My girlfriend once booked a private sauna for us. She gave me the most **amazing naked massage**. Then, when we were both **drenched in sweat and oil**, she slipped onto my lap and rocked her way to orgasm.